Independence, safety, and confidence!

Irene van der Zande
Illustrated by Amanda Golert

SKILLS FOR LIFELONG SAFETY AND SUCCESS

A publication of Kidpower Teenpower Fullpower International

Copyright And Permission To Use Information

Kidpower Teenpower Fullpower International
Office   831-426-4407 or (USA) 1-800-467-6997
E-mail   safety@kidpower.org
Web page   www.kidpower.org
Address   P.O. Box 1212, Santa Cruz, CA 95061, USA

Table Of Contents

Welcome To Kidpower!

Thank you for joining us in learning and sharing People Safety ideas and skills for yourself and others. We use the term "People Safety" to mean people being safe with their feelings and bodies with each other and with themselves. *Kidpower Youth Safety Comics* was created for young people ages 9 to 14 years old who are becoming more independent—and their adults. However, most of this information is relevant for people of all ages.

The more that everyone in a family, school, or youth group has a common understanding about safety, the safer they are. For this reason, we recommend that all the adults, teens, and older kids you care about read this book, discuss these ideas, and practice these skills with each other.

Make a commitment to safety!
Adults, please discuss the Kidpower Protection Promise on page 8 with your kids—and kids, please make the Kidpower Put Safety First Commitment for yourself and others on page 9.

How to learn and teach People Safety Skills
Go over the Discussions and Practices on pages 60 to 68. Whether you are reading this book for yourself or to help others to learn, please remember:

- **Learning and practicing People Safety is best done in a way that is fun and useful rather than scary or overwhelming.** Focus on skills and ways to be as safe as possible rather than dwelling on all the bad things that might happen. Through calm conversations, fun hands-on practice, and enthusiastic encouragement, we can learn how to stay safe most of the time.

- **People learn better by doing than by being told what to do.** As much as you can, give yourself and those important to you chances to practice every skill shown in this book. Take the time to role-play the situations that happen in the stories. Think about and discuss what the characters say and do to keep themselves and others safe.

Use People Safety in your everyday life.
Here's what we can do to help each other stay safe.

- Coach each other to be successful in avoiding and solving problems with people—in the same way that you might learn to be safe with water, food, fire, cars, and bikes—at home, in your neighborhood, in nature, at school, at work, and in your community.

- Growing up is hard on everyone. As young people become more independent, life often gets more challenging. Work together to keep relationships healthy and strong in your family. Encourage each other to be with respectful, kind, and supportive friends. Take responsibility for the safety and well-being of yourself and others.

- Listen to young people and show them that they are important to you. The best way to help young people stay safe is for them to have caring adults who they trust will listen and help when they have a problem. No matter how busy you are, ask kids calmly, "Is there anything you have been worrying or wondering about?" Listen to their answers without lecturing or teasing—and thank them for telling you. Instead of focusing on mistakes or what you think needs to change, tell kids often, "I love you just the way you are." And kids, if your adults forget to do this because they are busy or stressed, please remind them!

 A publication of Kidpower Teenpower Fullpower International® www.kidpower.org For permission to copy, contact safety@kidpower.org

How To Use This Book
These strategies and skills are important for people of all ages.

1. Encourage every adult and older child or teen you care about to read this book. Everyone is emotionally and physically safer when we have a common understanding about People Safety.

2. Discuss the stories, explanations, and examples. Notice how the young people in the drawings are using People Safety skills to prevent and solve problems.

3. Follow the *Discussion and Practices* directions on pages 60 to 68 to practice the skills together.

4. Remember to use your People Safety skills out in the world and with each other.

How Adults Can Help Kids Stay Safe

How to support young people in learning Kidpower skills.

1. Make a **Safety Plan for how to get help** everywhere you go. What changes with different people, at different times of day, and/or in different places?

I know you want to be in the mall alone while I shop. That is okay if you first tell me your plan, promise to check first before changing it, and show me your safety skills in case someone bothers you.

2. Ask questions to make sure everyone is clear about what the plan is.

Before you get on that airplane by yourself, I want to go over your safety plan. Who can you get help from if you have a problem?

I know! The flight attendant!

3. Set a good example. Solve problems peacefully, respectfully, and powerfully. Young people will learn more from what they see you doing than by what you tell them to do.

WATCH OUT you stupid @#+%!!!*

Excuse me. I am sorry. Goodbye.

4. Listen to kids. Respect their feelings. Don't lecture or tease.

Dad, I thought the movie was so cool, but now I feel silly. I am afraid of that monster we saw.

You're not silly, Miguel. You just have a great imagination. When I was your age, I was afraid of a lot of things. Let's think of a way to help you feel safe in your imagination.

A publication of Kidpower Teenpower Fullpower International® www.kidpower.org For permission to copy, contact safety@kidpower.org

Kidpower's Underlying Principle
The safety and well-being of young people are *more important* than anyone's embarrassment, inconvenience, or offense.

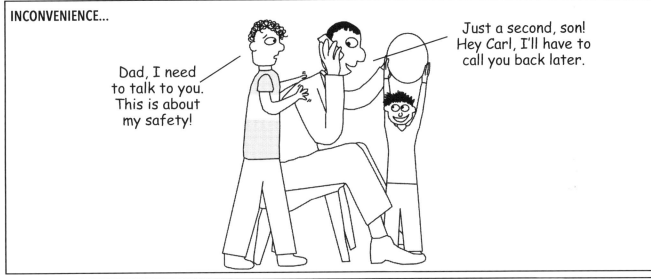

Make The kid**power** Protection Promise™

Imagine the impact if all caring adults discussed
this message with each young person in their lives!

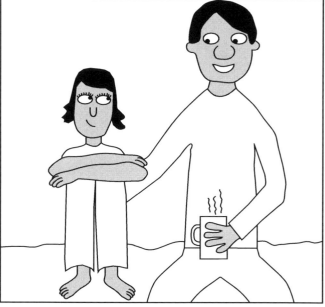

"YOU are VERY important to me. If you have a safety problem, I want to know–even if I seem too busy, even if someone we care about will be upset, even if it is embarrassing, even if you promised not to tell, and even if you made a mistake. Please tell me, and I will do everything in my power to help you!

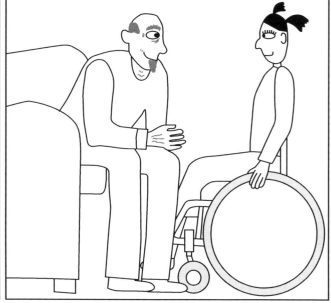

 A publication of Kidpower Teenpower Fullpower International® www.kidpower.org For permission to copy, contact safety@kidpower.org

Join Us in Making The
kid**power** Put Safety First Commitment!

"I WILL put the safety and well-being of myself and others ahead of anyone's embarrassment, inconvenience, or offense—including my own!"

Kidpower Means: Put Safety First!

To Put Safety First, walk away from trouble, set boundaries
with friends, make safe choices, and stop unpleasant touch.

1. Safety First means **walking away** from trouble even when someone is rude.

2. Safety First means that your right to say, "Please wait!" is **more important** than someone else's feelings.

3. Safety First means **keeping yourself safe** even if someone is hurt, upset, or in need. You can be caring by donating time and money to good causes.

4. Safety First means **speaking up** if you don't like the way someone is treating you.

 A publication of Kidpower Teenpower Fullpower International® www.kidpower.org For permission to copy, contact safety@kidpower.org

More Ways To Put Safety First!

Speak up about unsafe or disrespectful behavior, notice trouble, report problems, and know when to change your plan.

Stay Aware, Calm, Respectful, And Confident

Paying attention helps us to *notice and avoid* most trouble—and makes people less likely to bother us.

1. Kyle is not paying attention. This attitude is **less safe**.

Head down

Looking down

Body bent

Small steps

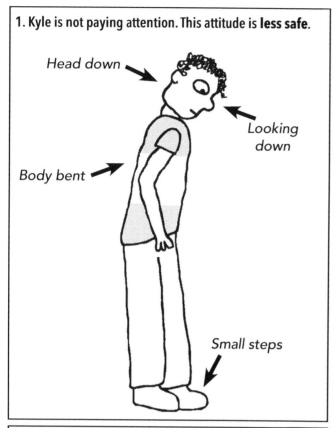

2. Kyle is aware and confident. This attitude is **more safe**.

Looking around

Head up

Body straight

Normal steps

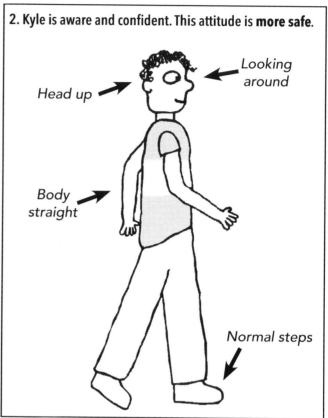

3. Lila is daydreaming. She is thinking about other things, and she is not looking around. This attitude is **less safe**.

Head in the clouds

4. Lila thinks about where she is going and what is going on around her. She is aware of the people, animals, cars, and other things around her. This attitude is **more safe**.

Looking around

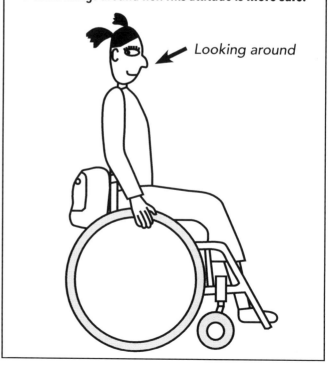

 A publication of Kidpower Teenpower Fullpower International® www.kidpower.org For permission to copy, contact safety@kidpower.org

Act Aware, Calm, And Respectfully Confident

You are safer if you *stay in charge* of what you say and do, no matter how you feel inside.

1. Marie Claire is feeling very angry. She has a tense face and is ready to get in a fight. This attitude is **less safe**.

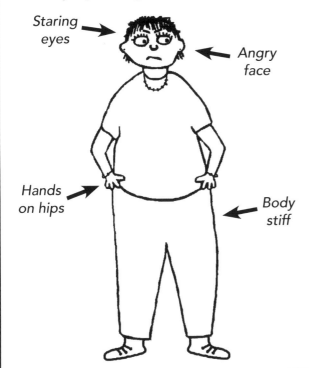

Staring eyes

Angry face

Hands on hips

Body stiff

2. Marie Claire calms herself down. Even if she is feeling angry inside, she can take a breath, relax her body, and act calm. This attitude is **more safe**.

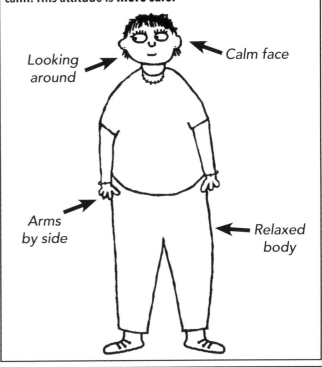

Looking around

Calm face

Arms by side

Relaxed body

3. Martin is feeling very worried and scared. He is trying to make his body small. This attitude is **less safe**.

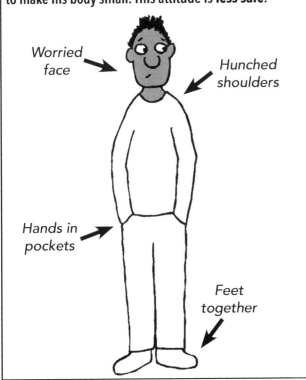

Worried face

Hunched shoulders

Hands in pockets

Feet together

4. Martin stands up tall and relaxes his shoulders. Even if he is feeling scared inside, he can look calm, aware, and confident on the outside. This attitude is **more safe**.

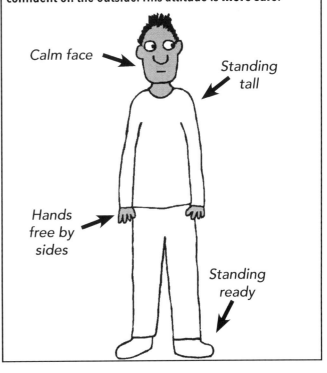

Calm face

Standing tall

Hands free by sides

Standing ready

Different Kinds Of Power

Take charge of safety with your Mouth Closed Power, Hands Down Power, STOP Power, and Walk Away Power.

1. A kid at school makes a rude remark to Martin. He knows that saying something mean back will **make the problem bigger, not better**. Martin uses his **Mouth Closed Power** and imagines throwing the rude remark away.

2. Marie Claire is curious about what a butterfly would feel like. She knows that touching the butterfly could hurt it, so she uses her **Hands Down Power** and looks instead of touching.

3. An older girl is trying to upset Lila by throwing mud on her clothes. Lila **yells "STOP!" and moves away**.

4. Kyle's older brother is trying to provoke him. Kyle's not in the mood to fool around, so he uses his **Mouth Closed Power** not to be rude back, his **Hands Down Power** not to hit, and his **Walk Away Power** to leave, and he goes into the house.

 A publication of Kidpower Teenpower Fullpower International® www.kidpower.org For permission to copy, contact safety@kidpower.org

Walk Away Story

Target Denial is a very powerful self-protection technique.
It means, "Don't be there!"

1. Kyle and Martin are friends. They like to play soccer together.

2. Kyle gets mad when he misses a goal or is losing the game. When he gets mad, he can act mean.

3. Martin knows that when Kyle gets very angry, it's best to **use target denial** and give him space to calm down.

I'll see you later...

4. Martin can play by himself or with other friends. Kyle can join when he is feeling calmer and can play in a safe way.

Moving Out Of Reach

Avoid getting tripped or shoved by Staying Aware,
Moving Out of Reach, Speaking Up, and Leaving.

1. An older boy at school is always pushing or tripping people. He trips Miguel and knocks him down.

2. Next time Miguel sees this older boy, he **moves out of the boy's reach** by making a big circle around him. He also **uses his awareness** by looking back so he can see if the boy is trying to sneak up on him.

3. Suppose the older boy tries to move closer and push Miguel. Miguel **puts his hands up in front** of him and says in a **calm, clear voice**, "Don't push me."

4. If the older boy yells at Miguel or calls him names, Miguel can **leave peacefully** and say something that doesn't provoke a fight like, "No, thanks" or "Bye." If Miguel needs help, he can always go and find an adult.

 A publication of Kidpower Teenpower Fullpower International® www.kidpower.org For permission to copy, contact safety@kidpower.org

Together Or On Your Own

Assess safety by noticing out in public whether you are
by yourself or whether there are people close by who can help you.

1. Jamila and Jenny are waiting for their movie to start. Someone is offering free pizza samples. There are lots of **people around**, it is **light outside**, and the **stores are open**.

2. Jamila and Jenny go get a free sample. The free pizza is very tasty.

3. Jamila and Jenny are waiting for their ride. It is dark now and the stores are closed. Someone comes up offering pizza. Jamila and Jenny **think about** whether or not it is safe for them to get a sample.

4. They decide to go inside the theater where there are **more people** around. They can look out through the doors to see when their ride is there.

Where Is Safety?

Safety is where there are *adults who can help you*. Your job
is to have a Safety Plan for how to get help everywhere you go.

1. Where is safety... When you are out with your friends at the park?

Our plan is to go over to the store where we are closer to adults who can help. Then, we can use our mobile phones.

If we need help right away, or if our phones don't work, we will ask for help from the storekeeper.

STORE

2. Where is safety... When you are going on a trip?

If we get lost, you can go to any of the security personnel, and they can page me over the loudspeaker. Here is our bus number and my cell phone number.

3. Where is safety... When you are out in nature?

If you see a hurt sea lion, move away quietly and get the ranger.

4. Where is safety... When you are at a friend's house?

OUCH! I cut my finger! It hurts really bad.

Let's get my Mom.

What Is A Stranger?

Although we might have scary pictures about strangers in our minds, remember that most people are good!

1. Most of us have heard a lot about what a stranger is. A stranger is just someone you don't know well.

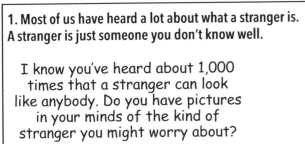

I know you've heard about 1,000 times that a stranger can look like anybody. Do you have pictures in your minds of the kind of stranger you might worry about?

Someone who takes you away!

A bad guy who hurts kids!

2. Miguel worries it would be someone who looks and acts scary.

Hey kid! Want some candy?

Someone who gives you poison candy.

3. Lila worries it would be someone who might look nice or who might act like they have a problem, but who would actually be trying to trick you.

Someone who tries to trick you into helping find his dog.

4. A stranger is just someone you don't know well. A stranger can be a man, woman, or child.

Those are things that **might** happen, which is why we have safety rules to follow with strangers. But most people are **good**. This means most strangers are **good**. In fact, we didn't know each other before and now we do. Why was it okay for you to be with me when I was a stranger to you?

Because our parents said it was okay!

How Do Strangers Become People We Know?

Check First with your adults if you are unsure about what safety rule to use!

1. When we **spend a lot of time** with someone, **sharing activities** together in person, we start to know this individual. Doing this **lots of times over many days** turns strangers into people we know well.

Those people are strangers to me. We haven't spent time together sharing activities like meals, games, and holidays.

2. You need to **Check First with your adults before you change your plan,** even with people you know. Sometimes doing something like taking a class with strangers *is* part of the plan you have made with your adults. Even then, any time someone bothers or worries you, getting help from your adults is important.

I'd like you to meet Carlos. He is going to stay with you until we get back.

Carlos is a stranger to me. It's okay to talk and be together because my dad said so.

3. Many people we **don't know well** are a regular part of our lives. We might know their voices, faces, names, or where they live. Even though they are acquaintances rather than strangers, **don't go with anyone until you Check First** with your adults about which safety rules to follow with them.

My dad lets me know what I can do with acquaintances. I have permission to go up to the mail carrier to get our mail, and I can talk to her. I can't go with her.

Lila, can you help me deliver some packages?

I wish I could help, but it's against my rules.

4. Even if someone is very nice or lives nearby, you still might not know each other very well. Ask your adults whether or not it is okay for you to be alone with that person.

Hi, Mopsy! Hi, Mr. Jones!

Hi! I am so glad you like Mopsy. I live round the corner. You can come visit him any time you want.

I don't know him well. I'll Check First with my adults before I go visit him.

You have to THINK FIRST about where it is that you met this person. A public place like a park, the sidewalk, the bus, or a store is different than a less public place like a home or classroom.

 A publication of Kidpower Teenpower Fullpower International® www.kidpower.org For permission to copy, contact safety@kidpower.org

Safety Rules For Personal Information

Personal Information is information about where you live or go to school, your name, and other things that are personal about you or your family.

1. Before talking to strangers, your job is to **Think First** about whether or not it is safe. Remember, you do not have to talk to a stranger. Talking is a choice. If you talk, do not give out personal information. If you are unsure, worried, or feeling unsafe, move away and Check First with your adult.

2. If a stranger asks you for **personal information**, you can **change the subject**, choose **not to say anything**, or **move away and get help** if you are worried.

3. Meeting people in the "real world" is different than meeting them online. The **people you meet only through the Internet are strangers**, even if you exchange lots of messages. Someone can pretend to be anyone online. **Think First** and ask your adults before giving personal information to anyone in chat rooms, gaming environments, interest groups, social sites, etc.

4. It can be okay to give out some personal information if you Think First about whether you have a **good reason** or if you have **Checked First with an adult you trust**. Talk with your adults about times when it is okay to give out personal information.

Thinking And Checking First

If you are on your own, *Think First before you take anything from, get close to, or talk to a stranger*. If you are unsure, worried, or uncomfortable, Check First with an adult you trust.

---

1. The rules are different when you are on your own, or when you are with adults who can help you. If you are on your own, your job is to **Think First** when you see someone you don't know.

Hi, Jenny. I'm Tim, from your old neighborhood. I haven't seen you in forever.

---

2. If you don't know someone, or are unsure, move away and **Check First** with an adult.

Where are you going?

Do I know him?

PET THE DOG!

---

3. Even if someone has something interesting to look at, or is upset, angry, or says he or she knows you, you still need to **Check First**.

Remember, we need to Check First before we get too close to someone we don't know well.

sigh

---

4. Your adult can help you to decide what is safe or not. Remember that **your safety is more important than anyone's embarrassment, inconvenience, or offense**. This means even if you forgot someone you used to know or hurt someone's feelings because you walked away, you are doing the right thing because your safety comes first!

There's a man named Tim who I don't remember.

Thank you for checking first!

 A publication of Kidpower Teenpower Fullpower International® www.kidpower.org For permission to copy, contact safety@kidpower.org

The Pizza Story

Check First with the adult in charge *before you change your plan* about where you are going, who is with you, and what you are doing, even if you know someone very well.

1. Chen and his sister are walking home after school.

2. Their dad drives up. He asks if they want pizza.
Let's get pizza!
Yeah, pizza!

3. Their mom is working at home. When her children don't come home after school, she gets worried. She tries to figure out where they are.

4. When their mom can't find her kids, she calls the police. They find the kids and their dad at the pizza parlor.
Hello, police. I am so worried. My kids aren't home, and I don't know where they are.

5. Mom is very glad and very mad.
WHY DIDN'T YOU CALL ME?!
We forgot. From now on, we will CHECK BEFORE WE CHANGE THE PLAN!

6. A few days later, their next door neighbor invites the kids to come over. They've been at his house before, but they remember to *check before they change their plans.*
Your mom says you can come over to my house for cookies.
We'd love to, but we need to Check First with Mom ourselves.

Miguel's New Bike

You are more important than your things.

1. Miguel has a brand new bike. He cares about it a lot and takes good care of it.

2. A man tries to take Miguel's bike. Miguel wants to go grab it from him, but he doesn't know the man, so he moves away and asks the man to put his bike down.

3. The man tries to get Miguel to come over to him. Miguel yells loudly and runs inside to get an adult to help him.

4. The man drops Miguel's bike, and his adults get it back for him. They are very proud of him for following his safety rules.

 A publication of Kidpower Teenpower Fullpower International® www.kidpower.org For permission to copy, contact safety@kidpower.org

The Stranger At The Door

It is important that adults remember the safety rules, too!

1. Marie Claire and her grandmother hear a knock on the door late at night.

2. The lady outside sounds scared and upset. Marie Claire's grandmother is worried about her and wants to let her in. Marie Claire reminds her grandmother of the safety rules and the importance of Thinking First.

3. They decide it is safer to call 911 for help rather than to open the door for someone they don't know late at night when only the two of them are there.

4. The police come and take the woman home. They tell Marie Claire and her grandmother that they did the right thing in calling them.

The Rules Are Different In Emergencies

If you are having the kind of emergency where you *cannot* Check First, your Safety Plan is to *get help*, even from someone you don't know.

1. Chen fell down on his skateboard and hit his head. Someone called an ambulance and a lot of strangers are trying to help him. He needs help and **cannot** Check First.

2. Chen sees a woman fall and get hurt. He knows that she needs help but he **can** Check First, so he runs into the store to get the storekeeper.

3. Jenny smells smoke in her house. She checks the door and it's hot, so she opens her window and yells. She needs help and she **cannot** Check First.

4. Someone dressed in a uniform asks Jenny to come and help fight a fire. She **can** Check First, so she runs to get her parents.

5. Jesse got lost on a field trip. A search party full of strangers is calling his name. Jesse **cannot** Check First, and he needs help.

6. Jesse is camping with his adults. A woman comes up with a photo of her child and asks him for help. Jesse **can** Check First, so he goes to get his family.

 A publication of Kidpower Teenpower Fullpower International® www.kidpower.org For permission to copy, contact safety@kidpower.org

When To Wait And When To Interrupt

You often have to wait when you want something. You interrupt and keep asking if you think you might have a safety problem, even if someone gets annoyed at first.

1. You have to wait in line when you want to return a book at the library.

2. You go to the **head of the line and interrupt to get help if you have a safety problem** like being lost or bothered.

3. Sometimes you have to wait for your adult to get something else done.

4. If something bad might be about to happen, **interrupt and make sure that your adult understands.**

Latisha Gets Help

Make a safety plan for what to do if you are bothered out in public.

1. Latisha had to go with her mother to the shopping mall. Her mother wants to buy office supplies, but Latisha would rather do something else. They agree to meet at the pet store in half an hour.

Remember your safety rules!

I know! Don't worry, Mom!

PET STORE

2. A nice-looking man and Latisha are both looking at the puppies. Latisha feels okay talking about the puppies. She is not giving out any personal information, there are lots of people around, and she is keeping some distance between herself and the man.

Aren't they cute?

Yes, they are!

PET STORE

3. The man starts to act scary, and Latisha protects herself.

Shh. Come with me, and you won't get hurt!

HELP! NO! This is NOT my Dad! Go away! Help!

PET STORE

4. The man runs away. Latisha goes to get help from the pet store clerk.

A man tried to get me to go with him! Please help!

I'm busy. I don't want to get involved.

5. Latisha makes the store clerk call the security guard.

I see you're busy, but I feel scared. You **have** to help me.

But he's gone. It won't do any good.

6. Latisha's mother comes back and finds out what happened.

You gave us such a good description that we found the man. He was bothering a little boy.

I am so proud of you. You kept yourself safe and kept that boy safe, too!

PET STORE

 A publication of Kidpower Teenpower Fullpower International® www.kidpower.org For permission to copy, contact safety@kidpower.org

Yell, Leave, And Get Help

If you are scared, yell using a loud, strong voice and quickly go get help.

Arm Grab Escape Story
Jenny uses her body and voice to be safe.

1. Jenny is walking her dog down the street. Some older boys from school are hanging around, and they whistle at her.

2. One of the boys grabs her arm.

Hey there, give me a big hug!

3. Jenny grabs her own arm and pulls away, yelling, "NO!" The boys are very surprised. She walks away quickly with awareness.

NO!

4. Jenny is going to tell her mom what happened right away. The boys never bother her again!

Introduction To Boundaries

A boundary is like a fence. It sets a limit.
Personal boundaries are the limits between people.

The rules about personal boundaries are:

1. **We each belong to ourselves.** You belong to you, and I belong to me. This means that your body belongs to you—*and* so does your personal space, your feelings, your time, your thoughts—*all* of you! This means that other people belong to themselves too.

2. **Some things are not a choice.** This is true for adults as well as kids. Especially for kids, touch for health and safety is often not a choice.

3. **Problems should not be secrets.** Anything that bothers you, me, or anybody else should not have to be a secret, even if telling makes someone upset or embarrassed. Also, presents, games, photos, videos, or any kind of touch should not have to be a secret.

4. **Keep telling until you get help.** When you have a problem, find an adult you trust and keep on telling until you get the help you need.

Physical Boundaries And Personal Boundaries

Personal boundaries help you to have better
relationships with more fun and fewer problems.

1. A boundary is a **limit**. There are boundaries you can see, like the lines on a soccer field or basketball court.

2. Some boundaries you can't see, but you can **feel**.

3. Your boundaries might be different with different people.

4. Your boundaries might change as you get older or as a situation changes. It is okay for something to feel good for a while and then feel less comfortable. **It is okay to change your mind.**

 A publication of Kidpower Teenpower Fullpower International® www.kidpower.org For permission to copy, contact safety@kidpower.org

Mean Word Disposal And Recycling

You can recycle the sounds and letters of hurtful words to create kind words for yourself.

1. Mean words and unkind body language can hurt our feelings and often make us feel angry or embarrassed. Instead of taking words or attitudes inside your heart and your head, you can think of ways of getting rid of them.

2. Chen uses the **Kidpower Trash Can**. He puts a hand on his hip and imagines the hole he makes is a Trash Can. He catches hurtful words and attitudes and throws them into his trash can.

3. After Chen throws the negative message away, he puts his hand on his heart and uses **positive self-talk** to help himself feel better.

4. Jamila makes the **Mini Trash Can** with one hand. She uses her thumb to push the word into her fist. The Mini Trash Can is great because it is small enough that you can do it behind your back or in your pocket, and no one would know you were doing it.

kid**power** Trash Cans And Recycling Machine

You can use different techniques to protect your feelings from unkind words and behavior.

1. There are many types of Trash Cans. Kyle makes one with two hands that he imagines is a dumpster.

You are so careless!

I care a lot.

Sometimes a Trash Can is just too small, so I imagine throwing the words into a dumpster. I am putting my hands and both fists together, and pushing my thumbs in like a dumpster. So, if someone tells me I don't care, I can throw those words away and say, "I care a lot."

2. Marie Claire makes a flip-top Trash Can.

(She's fat!)

I am beautiful just the way I am.

I like the flip-top Trash Can. If someone says that I am too fat, I can say, "I don't have to be thin to be beautiful and healthy!"

3. Miguel likes to just imagine a Trash Can in his head.

WIMP!

I feel very silly doing all these Trash Can things. So, I just use my imagination Trash Can. If someone tells me that I am a wimp, I can imagine throwing those words away and remind myself, "It is more powerful not to fight than to fight."

4. Latisha likes to think about it as recycling hurtful words into nice words. What ways can you come up with for dealing with hurtful words?

What we are really doing is recycling. All of these hurting words are made up of letters that we are recycling into kind things to tell ourselves.

 A publication of Kidpower Teenpower Fullpower International® www.kidpower.org For permission to copy, contact safety@kidpower.org

Jamila Protects Her Feelings

When people are unkind, *tell an adult you trust* so that you don't feel alone and helpless.

1. Kids at school make fun of Jamila. They call her names and talk behind her back. It really hurts Jamila's feelings, because she is a nice person and a good friend.

2. Jamila talks to her mom about how she is feeling. She hears the names kids call her in her head. She feels so embarrassed and like she is the only kid who is different.

3. Jamila and her mom talk about ways to deal with hurtful words. They practice throwing the words away. Jamila decides what words she wants to practice with.

4. Jamila feels ready to protect her feelings now that she has practiced with her mom. They also make a plan to work with the teacher to educate kids at school about respecting differences.

Taking In Compliments

Compliments are kind words that help you feel good about yourself.
When someone gives you a compliment, *take it inside your heart* and say, "Thank you!"

1. Joshua admires his older brother, who is feeling bad about himself. He throws away the compliment Joshua gives him.

2. Joshua knows compliments are nice words you should take into your heart. He tries again, and this time his older brother listens and takes the good words inside.

3. Latisha likes what her little sister built. Her little sister is feeling like what she made is no good. Her little sister throws the compliment away.

4. Latisha tells her little sister again and reminds her not to throw away compliments. Latisha wants her little sister to take the compliment inside.

 A publication of Kidpower Teenpower Fullpower International® www.kidpower.org For permission to copy, contact safety@kidpower.org

Throw Away Insults, Not Information

Even if people say something in an insulting way, it is
still important to understand what they want or don't want.

1. Kyle hates to do homework. He thinks it is a funny joke to throw away the word "homework."

2. His teacher tells him that of course this is not what the Trash Can is for.

3. Latisha's sister is mad at her and calling her names.

4. Latisha realizes that some of what her sister is saying is useful information. The other piece is an insult. She takes in the useful information and throws away the insult.

Separate Useful Information From Insults

Protect yourself to screen out hurtful words and listen for information.

1. Jesse is busy playing on the computer. His dad is frustrated that it is taking him so long to come down for dinner.

2. Jesses realizes he needs to **listen better** when his parents are talking to him. He **takes in the useful information and throws away the insulting** word "zombie."

3. Jamila is very interested in reading her book. She forgets to watch her little brother, and he knocks over the trash. Her grandmother is angry with her.

4. Even though Jamila doesn't want to take care of her brother, she knows it is important to keep him safe. She throws away the insult that she is lazy but takes in the reminder to watch her brother.

 A publication of Kidpower Teenpower Fullpower International® www.kidpower.org For permission to copy, contact safety@kidpower.org

kid**power** Consent Checklist

The safety rule is that touch or play for fun or affection should be the
choice of each person, *safe, allowed by the adults in charge*, and *not a secret*.

1. Touch and games for play, fun, or affection should be the **choice** of everyone involved. If Jesse doesn't want to be tagged, his friends need to stop.

2. Touch and games also need to be **safe**. Jamila loves to throw her baby brother into the air. He loves it too, but it is not safe when she lets go of him, so she has to hang onto him.

3. Touch and games also need to **be allowed by the adults in charge**. Kyle and his brothers are having a great time playing tag in the house, but it is against their mom's rules, so they have to stop.

4. When someone asks you to stop, it is important you **listen to them and stop yourself**, even if it is something you really like to do.

Choice And Not A Choice

You belong to yourself, but *often things are not your choice.*
No matter what, *anything that bothers you should never have to be a secret*!

1. Latisha fell and cut her hand. Even though she doesn't want to go to the doctor, she is hurt badly, and touch for your health is not a choice.

2. Miguel is very angry at Martin. He wants to hit him. Marco grabs Miguel's arm to help keep both of them safe. Touch for safety is not a choice.

3. Lila has the right to wish she didn't have to do chores, but the responsibility to help out anyway. Doing your chores, listening to the rules of your adults, and helping out in your family are not always a choice.

4. Marie Claire and Jenny are chatting in class. Mrs. Mullen tells them to be quiet. Following the rules at school or the laws of your community is not a choice, but also should never be a secret.

A publication of Kidpower Teenpower Fullpower International® www.kidpower.org For permission to copy, contact safety@kidpower.org

Secrets And Surprises

Fun surprises can be a secret for a while. Gifts, treats, favors, photos, videos, any unsafe behavior, relationships, touch, activities, and problems *should not be secrets*.

1. Good surprises that everyone else knows about can be secret for a while.

We are having a surprise party for Mom. So remember to keep it a secret.

This is a good secret that Mom will find out about soon.

SURPRISE!!!

2. Gifts should not be secret.

I'll get you those new shoes, but don't tell your Mom, okay? She doesn't like it when I buy you stuff.

I wish I could have those shoes, but I don't keep gifts a secret. Can we tell my Mom you got them for me for an early birthday present?

3. Treats should not be secret.

Let's get some ice cream, but don't tell your parents because they say I give you too many treats.

An ice cream cone would be great, but I don't keep treats a secret. We could just explain that it's a really hot day!

4. Favors should not be secret.

It is beautiful outside. Look, I'll do your report for you if you just come to the beach with me. Your parents never need to know about it. I'll make sure to write a great report so you'll get an A on it.

I know it would be a lot of fun to go to the beach, but I don't keep favors secret. Anyway, I know I am really supposed to write my report on my own. Maybe we could go to the beach tomorrow.

Other Times Not To Keep Secrets

Even if they will get upset, talking with your adults about what you want to do or about problems helps *increase their trust and your safety*.

1. Relationships should not be secret—even if others disapprove.

I don't keep friendships a secret. If my parents get upset, I'll explain that we are both being careful. I think that you should explain to your parents that there are safe ways to get to know people online.

Poprock: Don't tell your parents about our friendship because they will probably freak out—I know mine do when I meet people online.

Ferrari: I don't keep friendships a secret. If my parents get upset, I'll explain that we are being careful. You should explain to your parents that there are safe ways to get to know people online.

2. Touch should not be a secret.

I have some great stuff we can put on your shoulder that will make it stop hurting. I will just pull over and rub it on you. Let's not tell your parents because they might get the wrong idea.

No, thanks. Please just take me straight home. I don't keep touch a secret. I will ask my parents about what might be good to put on my shoulder.

3. Activities should not be secret.

My parents worry about the lake, but it's really fun there. I'll take you if you promise not to say anything.

I'd love to explore the lake, but I don't keep outings a secret. Maybe we can find a way to get your parents to let us go.

4. Problems should not be secret—even if you did something wrong.

You know we're not supposed to fight. I won't tell on you guys if you don't tell on me.

Our family safety rule is that we don't keep problems a secret. We are going to tell, even though our parents will be mad at us.

 A publication of Kidpower Teenpower Fullpower International® www.kidpower.org For permission to copy, contact safety@kidpower.org

kid**pow⊗er** Safety Rules About Private Areas

Even if thinking about this might be uncomfortable, knowing the
safety rules about your private areas can help to protect you from trouble.

1. Private areas are the parts of your body than can be covered by a bathing suit.

2. For play or games, other people should not touch your private areas or ask you to touch their private areas.

Let's take each other's clothes off. It'll be fun!

No. That's against my safety rules.

3. Sometimes grown-ups have to touch kids' private areas to help them.

OUCH! I need help to get these out!

4. Touch of any kind should **never ever** be a secret.

Marco had to pull thorns out of my bottom. I am too sore to sit down.

Thank you for telling me. That must have hurt.

5. People should not take or show kids pictures or videos of private areas unless it is for health or safety. Even then, videos or photos should not be secret.

What do you think of THAT?

They don't have any clothes on. Turn that off or I'll tell!

6. Even if a person stops, you should tell about anything that bothers you.

The new boy is trying to play games and show pictures that are not appropriate.

Thank you for telling me. I'll talk to him.

Stopping Unwanted Touch

Touch for affection or play should be the *choice of each person*. You can tell someone to stop if the person is touching you in a way you don't like.

1. Miguel likes hanging out with Roberto, an adult friend of his family. They watch movies together. Roberto always makes Miguel really good popcorn. Sometimes Roberto puts his arm around Miguel.

2. Most of the time Miguel likes sitting close to Roberto, but today he changes his mind. Miguel asks Roberto to stop by m**oving his arm away, looking him in the eyes**, and using a **strong, clear voice**.

> Roberto, please stop. I would like to have a little more room.

3. Roberto says okay, but he doesn't stop. Roberto isn't listening.

> Okay, but it is way more comfortable like this!

4. Miguel moves away to give himself a little space from Roberto. He **stands up, makes a fence with his hands**, and again tells Roberto to stop.

> I said stop. I want a little space.

 A publication of Kidpower Teenpower Fullpower International® www.kidpower.org For permission to copy, contact safety@kidpower.org

A bribe is like a trade where someone gives you something or does you a favor to get something from you in return. If someone tries to use a bribe to get you to **break the safety rules**, or asks you to **keep gifts or favors a secret**, that is **unsafe**. If you can't just leave, tell the person, "**Stop or I'll tell!**" If the person gets upset, you can tell an **emergency lie** by promising, '**I won't tell if you stop.**" And then, **as soon as you can, go and get help from an adult you trust.**

5. Roberto gets upset. Miguel doesn't want Roberto to feel bad, but he still wants him to stop. Miguel's **safety is more important** than Roberto getting his feelings hurt.

What's your problem? You're overreacting. I thought you liked hanging out with me.

Sorry. I like hanging out with you, but I want you to stop.

6. Roberto offers Miguel a bribe. He says he'll give Miguel a gift if he will just be more affectionate. Miguel knows Roberto is **breaking the rules** of his family. He sets a strong boundary.

If you'll just let me hug you, I'll take you to the skate park later, and I'll buy you that skateboard you wanted.

Stop or I'll tell!

7. Roberto gets very angry. He threatens Miguel. Miguel is alone with Roberto, and he can't just leave, so he says he won't tell if Roberto stops.

You'll tell? What a baby! I'm going to make tons of trouble for you!

I won't tell if you stop!

8. As soon as Miguel can leave, he **goes to get help** from his grandfather. They figure out what to do. Miguel knows it is o**kay to lie and break a promise *if* you are doing it to be safe and you tell an adult you trust right away**.

Abuelo, I have a problem. I need to talk to you.

Telling Or Tattling?

Tattling is when you are telling on someone just to get them into trouble. Telling is when you are trying to *get help to stay safe*.

1. Some older boys are pushing and teasing Miguel.

HA HA HA!

2. Marco starts to walk over to see what is going on. The boys threaten Miguel, Lila, and Jesse and say they better not tell.

Mr. Yard Duty is coming. Let's go!

None of you want to be tattletales, so keep your mouths shut or you'll be sorry!

3. Marco asks what's going on. Miguel doesn't want to be a tattletale, so he says everything is fine.

Is everything okay?

That's not what happened!

Yeah, I just fell down while I was playing tag.

4. Lila and Jesse want to get help. Miguel tells them not to say anything.

Those guys were being mean! We need to tell someone.

I am **not** a tattletale!

I don't want those guys to make us sorry. It's our word against theirs, and they're older.

5. Lila and Jesse decide it is important to get help anyway.

Those guys were pushing Miguel around. We don't want to tattle, but we are afraid they will hurt someone.

Tattling is not the same as getting help. I will keep an eye on them, and I will not tell them that you told me.

6. Next time the boys try to hurt Miguel, Marco is watching and makes sure the boys don't bother Miguel again.

HA HA HA! You look scared!

Hey! What's going on? You two are in **big** trouble!

 A publication of Kidpower Teenpower Fullpower International® www.kidpower.org For permission to copy, contact safety@kidpower.org

Jenny Persists In Getting Help Story

Persistence means *not giving up.* If you have
a safety problem, *keep telling until you get help*!

Advocacy Story

Advocacy means *persisting in speaking up* for
the rights, safety, and well-being of yourself and others.

A publication of Kidpower Teenpower Fullpower International® www.kidpower.org For permission to copy, contact safety@kidpower.org

Different Types Of Bullying

Bullying happens when people use their power to hurt you, scare you, or make you feel bad. You can use your People Safety Skills to protect yourself from bullying.

1. Bullying includes causing or threatening physical harm by kicking, punching, scratching, pinching, tripping, or pushing. Apologizing even if you did not do anything wrong can help to get out of an unsafe situation.

2. If someone is threatening or hurting you, move away. Set a boundary by saying, "Stop!" if this seems safe. Get help as soon as you can from an adult you trust.

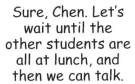

3. Teasing in a hurtful way is a type of bullying. This can be by trying to trip or knock people over, laughing at them, or trying to embarrass them. Sometimes we enjoy fooling around with each other, but it is only fun and okay if everyone is enjoying themselves.

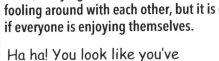

4. If people are teasing you, set a clear boundary and tell them to stop. Sometimes people have trouble listening at first. If they are not listening, move away and find someone else to be with for a while.

More Bullying Problems And Solutions

What to do if you are being left out or someone is trying to hurt your reputation.

1. **Leaving someone out is bullying.** This is also called shunning. Being left out can really hurt someone's feelings. It is okay to want to be alone sometimes or to just hang out with one person, but intentionally and regularly trying to leave someone out of a game or conversation is unkind.

2. If someone leaves you out, you can find someone else to talk to. If it happens a lot or is hurting your feelings, find an adult you trust to talk to who can help you come up with ideas on what to do.

3. **Trying to make other people dislike someone is bullying.** This can also include saying unkind things that are not true about someone and trying to make other people think less of this person. Making up mean things about people or spreading gossip that will hurt their reputation is not funny.

4. If someone says unkind or untrue things about you, speak up for yourself. Remember not to say hurtful things about other people. Making something sound worse than it was is untruthful. If people keep saying unkind things about you or someone else to each other, get help from an adult you trust.

 A publication of Kidpower Teenpower Fullpower International® www.kidpower.org For permission to copy, contact safety@kidpower.org

More Ideas For Noticing And Stopping Bullying

You have the *right* to be treated with safety and respect
and the *responsibility* to act safely and respectfully towards others.

1. **Making fun of people is bullying**. This means making mean jokes or teasing people about how they look or about something that bothers them. Joking around can be fun *if* everyone is having fun and *if* you stop as soon as the person being teased wants you to stop.

2. If people are teasing you, you can tell them clearly to stop. You can leave and find someone else to be with. If it hurts your feelings, you can use one of the Trash Can techniques or find another way to protect your feelings.

3. A very important way to stop and prevent bullying is not to do any bullying yourself! Don't do any mean teasing yourself and stop your friends when they do.

4. If someone is being left out, go and talk with that person. When you are hanging out in a group, don't let your friends intentionally leave someone out.

A publication of Kidpower Teenpower Fullpower International® www.kidpower.org For permission to copy, contact safety@kidpower.org

Speak Up And Get Help To Stop Bullying

Be a safety leader. Take action to create communities of respect and safety for everyone, everywhere.

1. If someone is being hurt or threatened, **speak up if you can do so safely**. Think about what you know about the person being mean. Is this the type of person who might stop if you are brave enough to speak up? Or is this someone who will probably get more mean or dangerous? If so, leave and get help.

2. If someone tries to make you feel bad about someone else, ask why and make sure you **talk to the person yourself**. People who gossip and say untrue things about one person are likely to say mean or untrue things about you as well.

3. People should be able to feel safe at school, at home, and out in the world. **Report problems** where people are being hurt, threatened, made fun of, or left out. Make sure you know **how to get help** at school and at home if you have a problem.

4. Bullying is mean and hurtful and happens to many people. Do what you can to stop bullying, and get help when you need it. Make good, true friends for yourself. Find caring, respectful adults who can help you. Be a good, kind friend yourself.

 A publication of Kidpower Teenpower Fullpower International® www.kidpower.org For permission to copy, contact safety@kidpower.org

Cyber Safety

You can take charge and make safe choices online just like you do in the physical world.

1. Online technology is great because it helps us share information and connect with people who are far away. It is important to talk to your adults about what the Internet and mobile technology rules are for your family.

It is so great I still get to hear how our cousin Sean is doing even when he is far away.

I'm glad! Now, I need the computer to help me figure out when the movie we want to see is playing!

2. The **people you meet on the Internet are strangers** to you. It is **not safe to give out personal information** in chat rooms or other Internet forums. **Check First** with adults you trust before giving out any personal information. Check First before going into chat rooms or answering an e-mail or instant message from someone you don't know in the "real world."

There is a really cute guy who says he lives nearby and goes to the same art program as me.

Remember what our rules are about the Internet. You don't know him, so you have to Check First with Mom before you give out any personal information.

3. The Internet is a great way to learn many different things, but a lot that you find is not true. **Double-check the source** on any sites where you are getting information, and **ask your adults** to make sure information is accurate.

Look, this website says this spider isn't dangerous and it won't bite. Let's get it to make webs from our hands.

Let's check some more websites and with my dad before we do anything else, just to make sure. Anyway, maybe that's not so nice for the spider.

4. Some things on the Internet are **not appropriate** for young people. Sites that say you need to be 18 years old to view them or have pictures of people without their clothes on are not okay for young people to **look at**. Do not open e-mails or look at websites that have pictures or information that is against your family's safety rules.

Oops! I didn't mean to get here!

OVEREIGHTEEN.COM

XXX

YOU MUST BE 18 YEARS OLD TO ENTER!!!

Protect Online Privacy And Stop Cyberbullying

How to prevent problems, avoid causing trouble, and get help.

1. Don't post or send anything into cyber-space that you don't want the world to see. This is true for e-mails, social networking sites, and instant messages, as well as text messages and digital photos on mobile phones. You want to be very careful what you write, say, or do, as it can get passed around to lots of people quickly.

Look how fast you can send a message! What a fun way to share stuff with your friends!

Remember, it is easy for anything you put on the Internet to get into the wrong hands, and then your private message or photo is not private anymore.

2. When people misuse technology to hurt or tease others, it is called cyberbullying. In some places, cyberbullying is against the law. Even in places where it is not against the law, people who are cyberbullying often end up in lots of trouble at school and at home.

Maybe it would be funny to you. But whether or not it is funny is not the right question. The right question is whether or not it would make someone else unhappy.

We could make up jokes and send out pictures about anybody!

It would be **so** funny!

3. Speak up if you see anyone cyberbullying and tell them that it is wrong. Get help from adults you trust if you need to.

We should send this photo of Marco to all of our friends! Look at how silly he looks!

We shouldn't send a photo that might upset Marco, even if it seems funny.

4. If someone bullies you with unkind words or pictures through e-mail, social media, texting, or other technology, **don't delete the message**. Save it, print it if you can, don't reply, and get help to report what happened!

That girl from the pool is really mad at me. She said she is going to tell everyone horrible things about me!

Save the e-mail and don't write back. Let's go tell your parents right away!

 A publication of Kidpower Teenpower Fullpower International® www.kidpower.org For permission to copy, contact safety@kidpower.org

Using Our Personal Power

Each of us has the power to stay in charge of what we say and how we act.

More Ways To Use Our Personal Power

We can take charge to avoid arguments, get help in an emergency, and support others.

1. We have the power to **stop ourselves** from saying or doing something hurtful or mean.

2. We have the power to **make our bodies move** or do something that is important even if we are feeling tired.

3. We have the power to **get help** for ourselves and others.

4. We have the power to do things to **help keep ourselves and others safe** even when we are feeling embarrassed, shy, or uncomfortable.

 A publication of Kidpower Teenpower Fullpower International® www.kidpower.org For permission to copy, contact safety@kidpower.org

kidpower Safety Signals for Everyone, Everywhere To Help Prevent And Solve Problems

Safety Signals are simple gestures, drawings, and words to
help all of us remember important People Safety ideas and skills.

Wait Power
Hold your own hands to show times when you need to wait patiently to stay safe and be respectful.

Stay Aware Power
Point towards your eyes, turn your head, and look around to signal how to pay attention and act alert.

Stay Together Power
Start with your palms apart and facing outwards, and then move them together to signal staying together to stay safe out in public.

Check First Power
Clasp your forearm with the other hand to show checking first with the adults who care about you before you change your plan.

Think First Power
Pat your head gently to show thinking first about what to do when the unexpected happens or someone is acting unsafely.

Walk Away Power
Use your fingers like legs and walk them on your arm to help you remember to walk away from any person or situation that might be unsafe

Roll Away Power
Roll your fingers along the other arm to show using wheels to roll away from trouble and get to safety.

Get Help Power
Put your arms in front of you with palms facing up like a bridge to show reaching out to get help or to make a connection.

kid**power** Safety Signals For Taking Charge Of Our Feelings, Words, And Bodies

The keys to remembering to use People Safety strategies and skills in real life are simplicity, repetition, consistency, fun, and practice.

Calm Down Power
Press your palms together, straighten your back, breathe deeply and slowly, and feel your feet to calm down

Mouth Closed Power
Squeeze your lips together to stop yourself from doing anything unsafe with what you say or do with your mouth.

Hands And Feet Down Power
Imagine you are about to bother or hurt someone with your hands or feet and then pull them down to your sides or the floor.

Hang On Power
To show stopping yourself from touching or hitting someone, hang onto your sides or pockets.

Speak Up Power
Put your hand in front of your mouth and move it outwards to show speaking up about what you do and do not want.

Fence Power
Put your arms in front of you waist-high with palms facing downwards to show making a fence to set boundaries with someone who is bothering you.

Trash Can Power
Put a hand on your hip and pretend the hole it makes is your personal trash can. Use your other hand to catch hurting words and throw them away.

Heart Power
Reach forward and then press your hands into your chest to show scooping kind words into your heart, protecting your heart, and using your heart to be kind to others.

A publication of Kidpower Teenpower Fullpower International® www.kidpower.org For permission to copy, contact safety@kidpower.org

kid**power** Safety Signals For Healthy Boundaries With People We Know

These Safety Signals help everyone, everywhere remember the boundary rules and principles for staying safe and having fun with people we know.

Safety Signals about The Four Kidpower Boundary Rules

We each belong to ourselves
Point to yourself, sit tall, and smile to show that each person's body, time, feelings, and thoughts are important.

Some things are not a choice
Shrug and smile to show that some things are required, and boundaries often have to be negotiated, even for adults.

Problems should not be secrets
Hold a finger in front of your lips. Now move the finger away from your mouth to show that we are safer when we can talk about our problems.

Keep telling until you get help
Pretend that your hands are talking to each other. One hand asks, "I need help." The other hand replies, "I will help you."

Safety Signals for the Kidpower Consent Checklist: "Touch, play, or games for fun or affection should be safe, the choice of each person, allowed by the adults in charge, and not a secret, which means that others can know."

Safe
Hug yourself to show that we all deserve to be and feel safe.

The choice of each person
Put two thumbs up to show that each person needs to agree about touch or games for fun or affection.

Allowed by the adults in charge
Curl up your fingers and move your hand up and down to show the head of the adult in charge nodding in approval.

Not a secret so others can know
Raise both arms above your head with your palms facing up to show that touch, play, and affection should **not** be a secret.

Discussions And Practices
To Build Understanding And Skills

Kidpower Youth Safety Comics provides tools for increasing the People Safety knowledge of young people ages 9 to 14 who are becoming more independent. This material is useful both for older children who are just starting to do a few things on their own, such as walking to a friend's house across the street, and for youth who are quite independent, such as riding their bikes to the neighborhood store, going to a movie alone with friends, or using public transportation.

How To Make Discussing, Practicing, And Using These Skills Successful

1. The more that everyone in a family, school, or youth group has a common understanding about safety, the safer they are. For this reason, we recommend that all the adults, teens, and older kids you care about read this book, discuss these ideas, and practice these skills with each other.

2. We will be safer and have better relationships if we keep using these skills in everyday life. Coach each other to be successful in avoiding and solving problems with people—in the same way that you might learn to be safe with water, food, fire, cars, and bikes—at home, in your neighborhood, in nature, at school, at work, and in your community.

3. Don't let discomfort get in the way of safety. Review your Safety Plans and the People Safety skills in this book on a regular basis. Give special attention to actions that might be hard due to embarrassment, such as interrupting busy adults when you have a problem, yelling to get help, or speaking up if someone is bullying. Remember that feeling embarrassed, upset, or shy is normal, but it is important not to let these emotions stop us from getting help or making the safest choices.

4. Stay relevant by adapting these examples and practices to make sense for each person's age, life situation, and abilities. If necessary, simplify the information by using fewer words, or change the wording to ensure understanding. You can also expand on the concepts presented by discussing with young people how to adapt these skills and ideas to handle more complicated situations that might not be covered in this book.

5. Instead of testing or tricking people, coach them to be successful. When you are practicing, pause to give people a chance to try to use the skill. If they get stuck, coach them in exactly what to say, how to say it, and what to do with their bodies, as if you were the director in a play. Encourage people to project an assertive attitude of both power and respect in their body language, choice of words, and posture, rather than acting either passively or aggressively.

6. Make the practices fun by being positive and calm rather than anxious. Reward small steps with encouragement, remembering that mistakes are part of learning. Celebrate progress rather than looking for perfection.

 A publication of Kidpower Teenpower Fullpower International® www.kidpower.org For permission to copy, contact safety@kidpower.org

7. Keep the focus on how to stay safe rather than on the bad things that can happen. Going into detail about the ways we can get hurt just makes people anxious without making anyone safer. Worrying and talking about safety problems can feel as if we are doing something—but are not nearly as effective as actually having a clear plan and practicing how to implement it so that we are prepared to take action.

8. Give discussing, practicing, and using these skills the same priority that you give other issues related to health and safety. These are crucial skills that can prevent problems and make daily life safer and more fun. If you encounter resistance, acknowledge that it is normal not to want to practice and to feel as if we already know what do so. However, rehearsing how to handle different kinds of problems is for our safety and must be a high priority. Discussing is not the same as actually practicing. Even if they express lots of resistance, most people also enjoy showing you and themselves that they know what to do.

The Kidpower Protection Promise (Page 8)

Adults, please discuss this message often with all children and teens in your life, making it relevant for their situations. Remind yourself to be a safe person for kids to come to by really listening with compassion even if a concern does not seem important to you or seems like their fault, without lecturing, scolding, or joking.

Make The Kidpower Put Safety First Commitment for Yourself (Page 9)

Kids, please make this commitment, "I WILL put the safety and well-being of myself and others ahead of anyone's embarrassment, inconvenience, or offense—including my own!" Discuss how this applies to real-life situations such as the ones shown in this book.

Directions for discussion and practices

At any age, we can all be students and teachers for each other—and you can even be your own teacher and your own student! The explanations below are for the person who is leading the discussion or practice. The students are the ones who are participating in these activities with the support of the leader. Page numbers in brackets.

Stay aware, calm, respectful, and confident (Pages 12-13)

Explain that "People will usually bother you less and listen to you more if you act aware, calm, respectful, and confident." Act out ways of being more and less safe. Now, coach students to practice walking with awareness, calm, respect, and confidence across the room. Stand behind them and do something silly for them to glance back and look at. Ask them to tell you what they saw so you know they are really looking around. Coach them to keep walking after they glanced to look back at you, to act neutral rather than with an attitude, and glance towards you rather than staring you down.

The ability to feel one way (e.g., scared or angry inside) and act another (e.g., aware, calm, respectful, and confident on the outside) is an important safety skill. Feeling worried or scared when someone is acting threatening, or getting angry if someone is calling you names, is normal. However, it is safer to stay calm and respectful on the outside, to leave, and to go and get help.

Use different kinds of power and move out of reach (Pages 14-16)

Discuss the many ways that people can be powerful. Coach students to squeeze their lips together to use Mouth Closed Power so that they are safe in what they say and do with their mouths. Coach them to lift their hands as they would if they were about to hit or to touch something they shouldn't. From that position, they can practice making the safer choice of putting their hands down at their sides to use Hands Down Power.

Coach students to put their hands in front of themselves like a fence and say, "Stop!" to use Stop Power. Have them practice using an assertive body language, tone of voice, and facial expressions rather than acting aggressive or passive. Pretend to be someone who is starting to get mad, or who is about to throw things or shove on the school yard, hall, or while waiting in line at a game or airport. Coach students to use their Walk Away Power to move out of reach.

Set up a practice where you pretend to be someone who often pushes or pokes other people. You stay in one spot and don't move. Coach students to walk past you while staying out of reach so that they have to move away and walk in an arc around you. Moving Out of Reach is an important skill, as even adults will often walk right next to someone even though they know this individual is the kind of person who bothers others, putting themselves in the way of trouble. Next, practice again and this time move one step towards kids one at a time as they are moving out of reach. Coach students to set a boundary and, in a calm, firm voice, say, "Stop." Remember, we want to have success-based practices, so stop when students set their boundary and coach them to continue moving away from you.

Thinking and Checking First Before you change your plan (Pages 22-23)

Even if they are independent enough to be out in public on their own or home alone without an adult with them all the time, young people are safest when the adults who care about them know where they are, who is with them, and what they are doing - including with people they know. They are safest if they assess the situation before they let someone they don't know well get close to them.

Practice how to Think First and Check First *Before* You Change Your Plan using relevant examples, such as: before you open the door; before you go with a friendly neighbor even if this is a kid who invites you to do something fun; and before you get close to someone you don't know well who is asking for directions, trying to talk with you, or trying to give you something. Pretend to be someone approaching the students in a friendly way and coach them one at a time to stand up, move away, and go to their adults to Check First or to Think First and call or text their adults to get permission before they change their plans. Now pretend that they are waiting for a ride and that you are someone they know but didn't expect coming to pick them up. Say, "Your ___ (mom, dad, adult) says to come with me." Coach students to move away and go to where they can call, saying, "I need to Check First for myself."

Stranger Safety (Pages 19-21 and 24-26)

Most young people know that a stranger is just someone they don't know well, but even adults often have images in their minds about what a stranger they are worried about might look like or how a stranger who will cause trouble might act at first. Discuss what students worry about when they think about a stranger, while you emphasize that a stranger is just someone you don't know well and that most strangers are good people.

As young people become more independent, they will be in situations where they can and should be able to talk to a stranger while they are on their own. Their job is to Think First before they take anything from, get close to, or talk to someone they don't know. What is important is that they stay very aware and assess the safety of the situation by noticing if there are a lot of people nearby to help them if they have a problem; by noticing whether someone is approaching lots of people or singling them out; and by not giving out any personal information.

Ask students to give you examples of personal information. Practice pretending you are a stranger out in public. Start out just saying hi or asking for the time. Next, ask a question that is personal information (e.g. "Do you live around here? Do you go to ___ school?"). Have students practice changing the subject or moving away if they feel worried or uncomfortable.

You can also practice by approaching students one at a time while calling their name or holding something that belongs to them. Even adults can be confused when a stranger says their name, because they think they may know the person. We want young people to Think First and Check First even if someone knows their name.

Kids and adults alike often have a hard time putting their safety ahead of their things. Tell students, "You are much more important than your stuff!" Explain that it safer to move away and get help than to try to get a possession back from someone who might cause trouble. Coach students to stand up, move away, and go to someone in charge to get help. As the pretend "stranger," act like someone who just doesn't know the safety rules rather than acting creepy.

Know your Safety Plan if you need help in public (18, 26-28)
Tell students, "Our goal is to know how to get help everywhere we go. Ask yourself, 'Where is Safety?'" Discuss where Safety might be in different places. If using a mobile phone is part of the Safety Plan, have a backup plan that involves talking to a person—such as asking a clerk for help, calling police, asking a woman with children, etc. Unless they are having a big emergency, young people should not leave the place their adults were planning for them to be.

Be clear that the rules are different in emergencies. Young people need to know what to do when they are hurt or in trouble, and they cannot immediately get help from their adults. Getting help from people you don't know well or at all can feel very embarrassing. Pretend to be a busy, impatient cashier. Coach students to act out coming to the front of the line, interrupting you, and being persistent in asking for help because they are being bothered by someone, their friend is hurt, or they are lost.

Discuss when to wait and when to interrupt. You might need to wait if you want something—but your safety plan is to interrupt even busy, impatient adults and be persistent in keeping asking if you need help. You can practice by pretending to be a busy adult and saying, "Blah. Blah. Blah." Coach students to interrupt you firmly and politely by saying, "Excuse me. I have a safety problem." Say, "I'm busy. Go away." Coach them to persist, "I see you are busy, but I need help!"

Yell, leave, and get help if you are scared (29)

Pretend to be someone acting unsafe by pointing at students one at time and yelling "Blah! Blah! Blah!" Coach them to put their hands in front of their bodies like a wall and to yell, "STOP!" As the pretend attacker, act startled and stop. Giving a response is very important to help students build their belief in the power of yelling. Coach them to run to Safety yelling, "I NEED HELP!" Have someone act as the Safety person they go to, and coach this person to say, "I will help you." Yelling in public can feel very embarrassing for people of any age. Model yelling in a loud, strong, and clear way yourself. Set a good example by yelling as loudly as you would want your loved ones to yell if they were in trouble. Practice yelling together to help everyone build strength and confidence in their voices.

Arm Grab Escape (page 30)

Practice the arm grab escape with students one at a time by grabbing one of their arms gently but firmly. When practicing, you are holding your students' arms hard enough so they feel a little trapped, but not so hard that you bruise them, injure them, or make it impossible for them to escape. The goal is for them to learn the technique.

Have each student stand up in front of you and grab their arm making sure there is enough room around you so you do not bump into things when practicing. Keep in mind that students will be pulling away from you so they need more space behind them. Coach them to clasp their hands together (make sure they are not intertwining their fingers) and use the leverage of their arm by turning and moving their body away and keeping their arm close to their body. When practicing they should loudly yell "NO" when they pull away—and then also practice going to safety.

The first time you practice, let go as soon as you feel a student pull against you. Kids can pull away with a lot of force so be prepared and make sure they are also in balance and prepared to catch themselves when they pull away. Then let the student practice again and hold on a little tighter. Coach students to pull their hands out against the place where your fingertips come together with your thumb, because this spot is the weakest part of someone's grip. Coach them to loudly yell, "NO!" and "HELP!" while pulling away.

Protect your feelings from hurting words (33-35)

Discuss with students the different kinds of words that hurt that others say to you or that you say to yourself. Act out using the different kinds of trash cans and affirmations shown in the drawings. For example, put a hand on your hip and show that the hole makes a personal Trash Can.

Practice together using language that is relevant for each person. For example, suppose that someone says, "You're stupid." Students can catch the word "stupid" and throw it into their personal Trash Can, and then put their hands on their hearts and say, "I am smart!" YOU be the one who is giving the insult for students to throw away—being sure that they are prepared to do this successfully—and have some positive self-talk ready to take care of their feelings. Don't let students be the ones who are giving the insults unless they can do this in a way that is emotionally safe.

 A publication of Kidpower Teenpower Fullpower International® www.kidpower.org For permission to copy, contact safety@kidpower.org

Ask students to come up with other positive ways to dispose of hurtful messages. Practice with words or attitudes that might be bothering them. The goal is to protect your own feelings while not being insulting to the person who was acting unkind, as this could cause a confrontation.

Now, practice giving each other compliments while the other person takes them in. In daily life, try to give each other genuine compliments as often as you can. Especially as children transition into becoming teens, they are often very hard on themselves and feel a lot of pressure to look and act a certain way. They need to hear over and over how proud their adults are of them and how much people love and care about them just the way they are.

Sometimes, when students learn the Trash Can technique, they want to throw away everything they don't like, such as having to do their homework, do chores, etc. Also, they find it confusing to handle a situation where an insult or negative comment is paired with a request for them to change their behavior or other important information. Review the examples on page 37 and come up with some other ideas about ways this happens.

The kidpower Consent Checklist is: Touch or games for fun or affection have to be okay with each person, safe, allowed by the adults in charge, and not a secret (Page 39)
Practice saying yes or no to touch and games by having students take turns saying, "Let's _____ (play tag, wrestle, have a race, or play catch)!" Coach them both to give and to respect different responses. For example, "That's great!" Or, "No thanks!" Or, "We'll have to go outside because we might break things inside." Or, "Not in the street!" Or, "Not at the dinner table!"

kidpower Safety rules about private areas (Page 43)
Acknowledge that this topic can be embarrassing. Discuss your safety rules and values in a calm and matter-of-fact way. Being able to talk about these issues with adults they trust is important in helping young people make safe and wise choices and in stopping unsafe behavior.

Stop unwanted touch or teasing (Pages 44-45)
Healthy boundaries about affection includes people being able to ask for what they want, accepting a no answer, realizing when they don't want some kinds of touch, and being able to say so.

To practice, ask for a hug and coach students to say, "No, thanks! Let's just wave!" Coach students to ask you for a hug so you can say, "No, thanks! Let's just shake hands."

Most people don't like being told what to do or not do. We need to know how to persist in protecting our boundaries in case someone doesn't notice, doesn't listen, tries to make us feel wrong by using emotional coercion, offers a bribe, or makes us promise not to tell. We need to be prepared to use our voices, bodies, and words to set strong and respectful boundaries with people we know, such as family, friends, and peers. In these practices, YOU take on the role of the person who is causing the problem, making sure that you are coaching students to be successful. Unless they can do this in a way that is emotionally safe, do not have students act out pretending to be the one who is pushing against someone's boundaries.

Pretend to bother students one at a time by touching them on their shoulders. Ask, "Do you like this? If you like this touch, it is fine. But can you change your mind? Yes, you can. Now, pretend you don't like this touch any more." Coach students to give you back your hand in a firm, polite way and say, in a clear, respectful voice, "Please stop."

Pretend not to listen, and put your hand back. Coach students to stand up and move back, make a fence with their hands, look at you, and say in a powerful and respectful way, "I said, 'Please stop!' I don't like it."

Next, pretend to be sad or annoyed so students can practice dealing with emotional coercion. Say, "But I like you. I thought you were my friend." Coach students to project an assertive attitude while they say, "I don't mean to hurt your feelings and I am your friend, and I still want you to stop." Or just, "Sorry and stop!"

Discuss when bribes are safe or unsafe. Practice resisting unsafe bribes. Say, "I'll give you a _____ (a treat, some money, or something else you think the person you are practicing with would like) if you let me touch your shoulder after you asked me to stop. But don't tell anybody, okay?" Coach each student to say, "Stop or I'll tell!"

Pretend to get angry or upset without acting intensely or making specific threats. Say, "Promise not to tell anyone or something bad will happen!" Or, "You have to promise not to tell or I won't be able to hang out with you anymore." Or, "Please don't tell, or I could get into trouble." Coach students to say, "I won't tell if you stop." Say, "Most of the time, our values are to tell the truth and keep our promises. But you can lie and break a promise to stay safe, as long as you get away as soon as you can and tell an adult you trust and keep telling until someone does something about it."

Telling (Pages 46-47)
Remind students that touch, games, presents, activities, photos, videos, and problems should not be secrets. Discuss different safety problems they might have and adults that they can ask for help if they need it.

To practice, tell students one at a time to pretend to have a safety problem. You pretend to be a busy adult (act as if you are reading a book, texting, or working). Coach students to interrupt you to ask for help. Say, "I'm busy." Coach them to ask again. Say, "Don't bother me." Coach them to say, "This is about my safety." Listen and coach them to tell the whole story. Say, "Thank you for telling me." If students do this well, do the practice again but be unsupportive by saying, "That's your problem. Solve it yourself." Coach them to persist and say, "I tried solving it myself but I don't feel safe. I need help." If this doesn't work, remind them to find another adult to tell.

Tell young people, "Remember that it is not your fault if you have a safety problem even if you made a mistake and that it is never too late to tell, so keep telling until you get help."

Advocacy Skills (48)
Simple advocacy or bystander intervention skills can prepare people to prevent violence or harassment of others, including for animals that can't speak up for themselves. Discuss ideas about how and when we can safely speak up for others—and other ways to support them if we can't do something in the moment.

 A publication of Kidpower Teenpower Fullpower International® www.kidpower.org For permission to copy, contact safety@kidpower.org

Know what bullying is and how to stop it (pages 49 to 52)

Point out examples of bullying, teasing, and harassment as they happen in real life, in stories, in games, or in movies, such as shunning, name-calling, intimidation, etc. Pretend to act like someone who is bullying by saying something mean. Coach students to use their Trash Cans and move away. Or, coach them to say, "Stop," to leave, and to get help.

Lead a practice about inclusion. First, practice persisting. Pretend to be playing a game and or having a discussion. Coach students one at a time to walk up to you and say in a cheerful, assertive way, "Excuse me. I'd like to join you." Act out being rejecting by frowning and saying, "Go away. We don't want you here." Or, "You're not good enough." Or, "There are too many playing already." Coach kids to practice persisting using a calm, clear tone of voice, instead of getting upset. For example, "I'd really like to join you." Or, "I'll get better if I practice." Or, "There's always room for one more." Or, "Give me a chance." Or, "The rule here is everybody gets to participate."

Now, practice leaving. Pretend to be leaving students out and coach them to leave with confidence, approach someone else who seems to be alone, and reach out in a friendly and confident way by asking, "Do you mind if I join you?" Have that person respond by saying cheerfully, "Sure!"

Now, practice advocacy skills. Pretend to be unkind to someone else. Coach students to say, "Stop. That is not kind!" Or, "That's a hurtful thing to say. Please stop!" Or, "Let her play!"

Pretend to be someone who is bullying physically. One at a time, push students gently and say something like, "What's wrong with you, dummy!" Coach them to take a breath, throw the mean word away, use Mouth Closed Power by not answering back, and use Walk Away Power by standing tall, staying calm, and walking with awareness. Remind young people to go to an adult in charge and get help because problems should not be secrets.

Cyber Safety (pages 53 to 54)

Please use these pages to facilitate a discussion with your family, school, or organization about your safety rules regarding use of the Internet, mobile phones, and computers. Discuss with young people what kinds of skills could work in the situations shown, as well as others.

Personal Power (pages 55 to 56)

We each have the power to make our own choices. It can feel as if we can't stop ourselves or that something is too embarrassing to do, but in each of us, we have the strength to overcome resistance to make safer choices. Coach young people to imagine they are feeling very embarrassed and practice getting help anyway; to stop themselves if they feel like saying something mean; and to know how to make their bodies move faster, even if they are very tired.

Kidpower Services For All Ages And Abilities

Kidpower Teenpower Fullpower International is a global nonprofit leader dedicated to providing effective and empowering child protection, positive communication, and personal safety skills for all ages and abilities. Since 1989, Kidpower has served millions of children, teenagers, and adults, including those with difficult life challenges, locally and around the world through our in-person workshops, educational resources, and partnerships. We give our students the opportunity for successful practice of "People Safety" skills in ways that helps prepare them to develop healthy relationships, increase their confidence, take charge of their emotional and physical safety, and act safely and respectfully towards others. For more information, visit www.kidpower.org or contact safety@kidpower.org.

Workshops
Through our centers and traveling instructors, Kidpower has led workshops in over 60 countries spanning six continents. Our programs include: Parent/Caregiver seminars; Parent-Child workshops; training for educators and other professionals; classroom workshops; Family workshops; Teenpower self-defense workshops for teens; Collegepower for young people leaving home; Fullpower self-defense and boundary-setting workshops for adults; Seniorpower for older people; adapted programs for people with special needs; and workplace safety, communication, and team-building seminars. Our three-day Child Protection Advocates Training Institute prepares educators and other professionals, as well as parents and other caring adults, to use Kidpower's intervention, advocacy, and personal safety skills in their personal and professional lives.

Online Library
Our extensive online Library provides over 400 free People Safety resources including articles, videos, webinars, blogs, and podcasts. Free downloads of online publications like our Kidpower Safety Signals, coloring book, and handouts are available for individual use. We provide licensing for use of materials or content for charitable and educational purposes.

Coaching, Consulting, and Curriculum Development
Long-distance coaching by video-conferencing, telephone, and e-mail enables us to make our services accessible worldwide. We consult with a wide range of experts, organizations, and schools on how best to adapt our program to meet unserved needs and develop new curriculum to increase the People Safety knowledge for different people facing difficult life challenges.

Instructor Training and Center Development
Our very comprehensive certified instructor training program prepares qualified people to teach our programs and to establish centers and offices for organizing services in their communities under our organizational umbrella.

Kidpower Books

We publish an extensive preschool through high school curriculum, as well as books about personal safety for adults. Please visit **kidpower.org/books** for complete information.

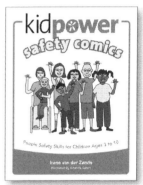

Acknowledgments

Kidpower is a tapestry of many different threads woven by many different hands. Our curriculum has grown from the ideas, questions, teaching, feedback, and stories of countless people since I first started working on child protection, personal safety, and self-defense issues in 1985.

I want to express my appreciation to each of our Kidpower instructors, board members, honorary trustees, senior program leaders, center directors, workshop organizers, advisors, volunteers, donors, parents, students, funding partners, service partners, family members, advocates, hosts, and office staff.

Thank you for the thought, care, time, and generosity that you have given to bring Kidpower Teenpower Fullpower International to where we are today. I feel honored to have you as colleagues and as friends.

Writing each person's story would be a book unto itself. You can learn about the remarkable people who have built and keep building our organization by reading *A Tapestry Woven By Many Different Hands* on our website.

I want to give special acknowledgment to people who have helped to create our cartoon-illustrated *Safety Comics* and *Teaching Books* series in many different ways.

Amanda Golert is a Senior Program Leader, Training and Curriculum Consultant, and our Sweden Center Director since 1999. Amanda's role has been crucial in the development of all of our cartoon-illustrated books as the artist, designer, and primary editor.

Timothy Dunphy, our Program Co-Founder, worked with me for many years to create our curriculum and still teaches and serves as a member of our training team.

Senior Program Leader **Chantal Keeney** provided major help with editing, teaching instructions, and content development of our original cartoon-illustrated curriculum.

Our California Program Director **Erika Leonard**; Montreal Center Director **Marylaine Léger**; New Zealand Center Co-Director **Cornelia Baumgartner**; Colorado Center Director **Jan Isaacs Henry**; and Chicago Center Director **Joe Connelly**, who also are all Senior Program Leaders, have each contributed important ideas and improvements to these Kidpower social stories, explanations, and skills over the years.

Finally, thank you to Kidpower Instructor and Senior Program Leader **John Luna-Sparks**, LCSW, CMP, for many years of support, including working with me to create our original Safety Signals.

Thank you to each of the remarkable people from around the world for your gifts of commitment, creativity, time, talent, and generosity!

About The Author

Irene van der Zande is the Founder and Executive Director of Kidpower Teenpower Fullpower International, a global non-profit leader dedicated to protecting people of all ages and abilities from bullying, violence, and abuse by empowering them with knowledge and skills.

Since 1989, Kidpower has served over 5.5 million children, teenagers, and adults, including those with special needs, through its positive and practical workshops, extensive free online Library, and publications.

Since Kidpower began, Irene has led the development of programs, training of instructors, and establishment of centers, working with a wide range of international experts in education, public safety, violence prevention, mental health, and the martial arts.

Irene has authored numerous books and articles in the child development, child protection, positive communication, and violence and abuse prevention and intervention fields, including the following:

The Parent/Toddler Group: A Model of Effective Intervention to Facilitate Normal Growth and Development, which is published by Cedars-Sinai Medical Center and used as a textbook for mental health and child education professionals; *1, 2, 3... The Toddler Years: A Guide for Parents and Caregivers*, which is used as a textbook in early childhood development programs in many colleges and has a foreword by early childhood development and Respect for Infant Educarers founder Magda Gerber; *The Kidpower Book for Caring Adults*, a comprehensive guide on personal safety, self-protection, confidence, and advocacy for young people; *Bullying: What Adults Need to Know and Do To Keep Kids Safe*, which is used in the anti-bullying programs of many families, schools, and youth organizations; and the cartoon-illustrated *Kidpower Safety Comics Series* and *Preschool to Young Adult Curriculum Teaching Books*, which provide entertaining and effective tools for introducing and practicing safety skills with young people.

About The Illustrator

Amanda Golert is an experienced self-defense instructor, trainer, passionate advocate for personal safety for children and other vulnerable people, the Center Director of Kidpower Sweden—and she also likes to draw!

Since 1999, Amanda has supported the growth and development of Kidpower Teenpower Fullpower International. She works in partnership with Irene to illustrate, edit, and design the Kidpower cartoon books and many other educational materials.

Made in the USA
Las Vegas, NV
10 March 2022

45406708R10039